DE RED HAT

By Madison Johnson
Illustrated by Michael Magpantay

Library For All Ltd.

Library For All is an Australian not for profit organisation with a mission to make knowledge accessible to all via an innovative digital library solution. Visit us at libraryforall.org

Deb's Red Hat

First published 2021

Published by Library For All Ltd
Email: info@libraryforall.org
URL: libraryforall.org

This book was made possible by the generous support of the Education Cooperation Program.

Original illustrations by Michael Magpantay

Deb's Red Hat
Johnson, Madison
ISBN: 978-1-922763-51-8
SKU01822

DEB'S RED HAT

Deb puts on her red hat and skips up the hill to sit by the pond.

She sits on a rock and gives the ducks a snack.

A gust spins Deb's red hat up.

She checks in the sand box, but the red hat is not there.

She runs to the bus stop, but the red hat is not there.

Deb jogs to the dock on the pond by the snack shop, but the red hat is not there.

Deb sits to rest on a
stump and sobs.

Deb hears a trill from a finch on a branch. Deb scans up.

Deb spots her red hat on a twig.

Deb is glad and skips back with her red hat.

You can use these questions to talk about this book with your family, friends and teachers.

 What did you learn from this book?

 Describe this book in one word. Funny? Scary? Colourful? Interesting?

 How did this book make you feel when you finished reading it?

 What was your favourite part of this book?

About the author

Madison Johnson teaches Grade 1 in Smiths Station, Alabama, USA. She has been teaching for five years and graduated from Auburn University with a Bachelor's degree in Elementary Education. She wrote this decodable story to help young children learn to read with short vowel sounds. She hopes you enjoy her story!

Did you enjoy this book?

We have hundreds more expertly curated original stories to choose from.

We work in partnership with authors, educators, cultural advisors, governments and NGOs to bring the joy of reading to children everywhere.

Did you know?

We create global impact in these fields by embracing the United Nations Sustainable Development Goals.

libraryforall.org

9 781922 763518